SALT WATER TAFFY

THE SEASIDE ADVENTURES OF JACK & BENNY

SALT WATER TAFFY™

THE SEASIDE ADVENTURES OF JACK & BENNY
VOL 1: "THE LEGEND OF OLD SALTY"

Written & Illustrated by
Matthew Loux

Lettered by Douglas E. Sherwood
Design by Matthew Loux & Steven Birch @ Servo
Edited by Randal C. Jarrell

Published by Oni Press, Inc.

Joe Nozemack, publisher

James Lucas Jones, editor in chief

Randal C. Jarrell, managing editor

Keith Wood, art director

Cory Casoni , director of marketing

Doug Sherwood, production assistant

Jill Beaton, assistant editor

ONI PRESS, INC.
1305 SE Martin Luther King Jr. Blvd.
Suite A
Portland, OR 97214
USA

www.onipress.com
www.actionmatt.com

First edition: May 2008
ISBN-13: 978-1-932664-94-2

10 9 8 7 6 5 4 3 2
PRINTED IN CANADA.

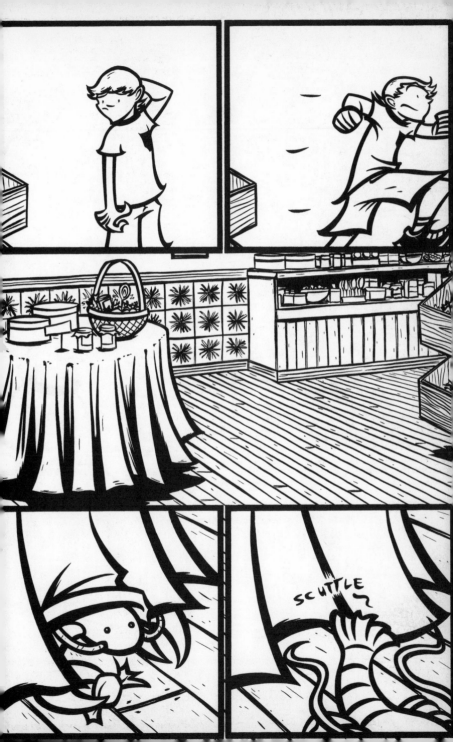

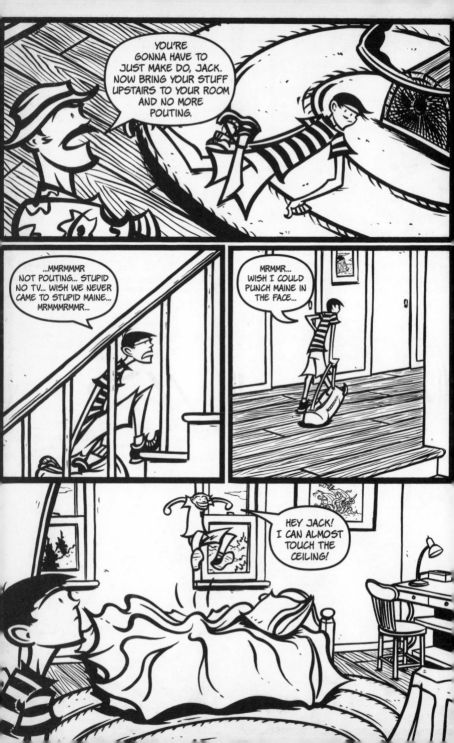

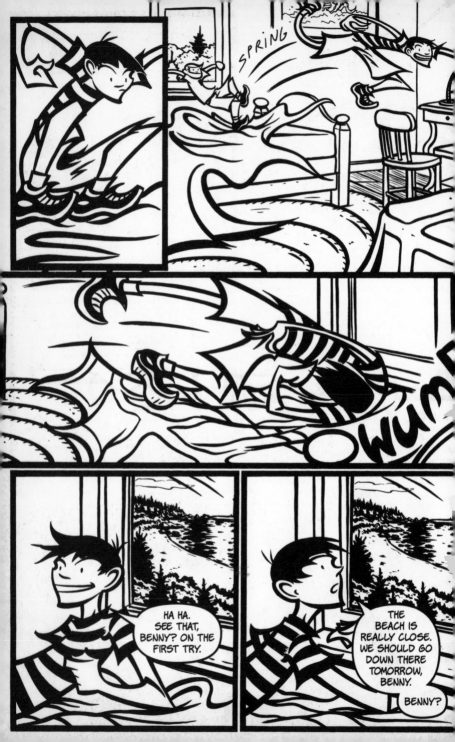

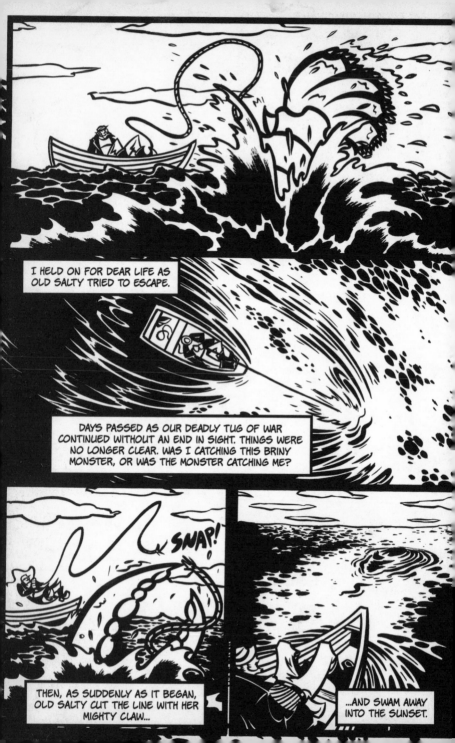

I HELD ON FOR DEAR LIFE AS OLD SALTY TRIED TO ESCAPE.

DAYS PASSED AS OUR DEADLY TUG OF WAR CONTINUED WITHOUT AN END IN SIGHT. THINGS WERE NO LONGER CLEAR. WAS I CATCHING THIS BRINY MONSTER, OR WAS THE MONSTER CATCHING ME?

SNAP!

THEN, AS SUDDENLY AS IT BEGAN, OLD SALTY CUT THE LINE WITH HER MIGHTY CLAW...

...AND SWAM AWAY INTO THE SUNSET.

SNAP!

HEY BENNY! I FOUND A GOOD ONE HERE!

HERE'S MINE.

THAT WON'T WORK. THERE'S TOO MUCH STUFF ON IT.

IT'LL WORK. I HAVE A PLAN.

OH REALLY?

DID YOU HEAR THAT?

YEAH...

RUSTLE

...OLD SALTY?

BENNY, OLD SALTY'S NOT REAL...

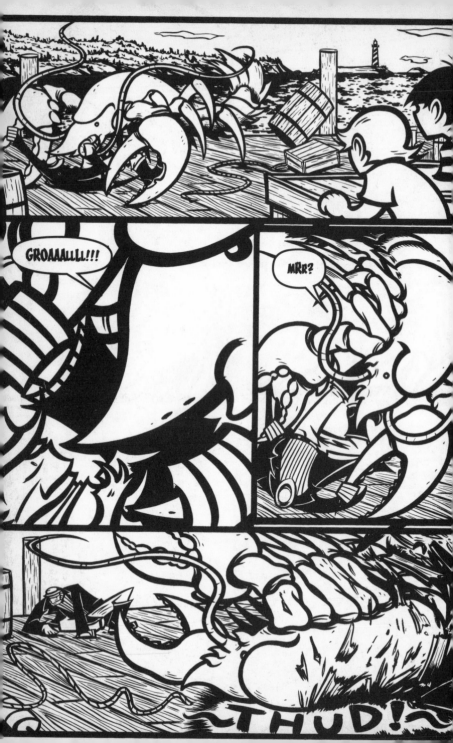

CRASH

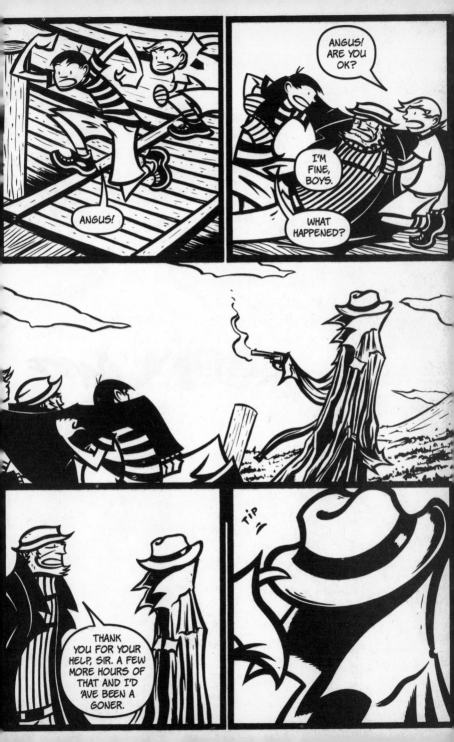

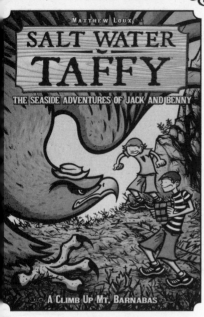
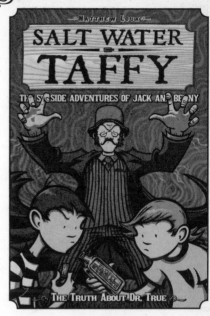

Matthew Loux grew up in eastern Connecticut and spent many a vacation along the New England coastline. He attended the School of Visual Arts in New York City and currently resides in Brooklyn.

actionmatt.com

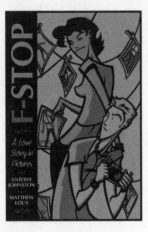